fAll

D0198785

BANG THE DRUM

Written by
KATE RUTTLE

Illustrated by
BECCY BLAKE

WAYLAND

First published in 2011
by Wayland

This paperback edition published
in 2012 by Wayland

Text copyright © Kate Ruttle 2011

Illustration copyright © Wayland 2011

Wayland
338 Euston Road
London NW1 3BH

Wayland Australia
Level 17/207 Kent Street
Sydney, NSW 2000

The rights of Kate Ruttle to be identified as the
Author of this Work has been asserted by her
in accordance with the Copyright, Designs
and Patents Act, 1988.

All rights reserved.

Series editor: Louise John
Designer: Paul Cherrill
Consultant: Kate Ruttle

A CIP catalogue record for this book is
available from the British Library.

ISBN 9780750266499

Printed in China

Wayland is a division of Hachette Children's Books,
an Hachette UK company.
www.hachette.co.uk

FIZZ WIZZ PHONICS is a series of fun and exciting books, especially designed to be used by children who have not yet started to read.

The books support the development of language, exploring key speaking and listening skills, as well as encouraging confidence in pre-reading skills.

BANG THE DRUM is all about instrumental sounds. The book follows a group of children as they explore the traditional song, 'I am the Music Man, and I come from down your way'. The children play a variety of instruments, focusing on the different sounds they can hear.

For suggestions on how to use **BANG THE DRUM** and further activities, look at page 24 of this book.

The Music Man

I am the Music Man,
and I come from down your way,
and I can play...

What can you play?
I can play my instruments!

Boom, Boom!

I am the Music Man,
and I come from down your way,
and I can play...

6

Boom
Boom

What can you play?
I can play the big drum.

Toot, Toot!

I am the Music Man,
and I come from down your way,
and I can play...

Toot Toot

What can you play?
I can play the silver flute.

Swish, Swish!

I am the Music Man,
and I come from down your way,
and I can play...

What can you play?
I can play the maracas.

Oompa, Oompa!

I am the Music Man,
and I come from down your way,
and I can play...

Oompa
Oompa

What can you play?
I can play the tuba.

Jingle, Jingle!

I am the Music Man,
and I come from down your way,
and I can play...

Jingle Jingle

What can you play?

I can play the tambourine.

Twang, Twang!

I am the Music Man,
and I come from down your way,
and I can play...

Twang
Twang

What can you play?
I can play the guitar.

Ting, Ting!

I am the Music Man,
and I come from down your way,
and I can play...

Ting Ting

What can you play?
I can play the finger cymbals.

Tinkle, Tinkle!

I am the Music Man,
and I come from down your way,
and I can play...

Tinkle
Tinkle

What can you play?
I can play the piano.

A Big Band

I am the Music Man,
and I come from down your way,
and I can play...

What can you play?
I can play in a big band.

Further Activities

 These activities can be used when reading the book one-to-one, or in the home.

 These activities can be used when using the book with more than one child, or in an educational setting.

P4 • Can you sing the song, 'I am the Music Man'.

P6 • Does the drum on this page make a loud noise or a soft one? What's happening in the picture to tell you this?
• Use a wooden spoon and try hitting some suitable objects in the house. Which makes the best drum sound?

P8 • Look at the pictures. Point out that you play the flute by blowing over the top of it, like you blow over the top of a bottle.
• Try blowing over the top of an empty glass bottle. Can you make a sound?
• Try to make the sound of a flute with your voice.

P10 • Make your own shakers. Put rice and salt into different pots and seal them with kitchen foil and elastic bands.
• Play the shakers and listen to the sounds. Are they all the same? Can you tell which is which?

P12 • Look at the pictures of the tuba. Talk about what sound it makes. Use words such as 'low' and 'deep' to describe the sound. Can you make your voice deep?
• Try puffing very hard with big cheeks to blow out a sound through closed lips. What kind of sound does it make?

P14 • Make a paper-plate tambourine. Put holes around the edge of the plate and attach threaded milk-bottle tops. Try shaking it and hitting it. Are the sounds the same or different?
• Play your instrument while you dance to your favourite music.

P16 • Can you mimic the action of playing the guitar?
• Find a music video which includes a guitar. Watch how the guitarist plays. Can you hear the guitar music?

P18 • Look at the picture of the Music Man. The little cymbals he is holding are from India. Can you find India on a map?

P20 • Listen to some music of a classical piano concerto. Can you move your fingers as quickly as the pianist?

P22 • Look at the picture of the Music Man. Can you match each of his instruments with one that a child in the picture is playing?
• Try to remember what each of the instruments is called. Mime how to play them together.

P4 • Find as many instruments as possible. Have a go at playing them
• Look at some sheet music. Can you see how the notes on the page tell people how to play an instrument?

P6 • Gently tap parts of your own body. Which parts makes the best drum sound?
• Put rice on top of a drum. What happens when you hit the drum? Talk about why.

P8 • How do you make a sound out of a flute? Do you hit it, shake it or blow down it?
• Go online to find a sound file of a flute being played. Is the music smooth or jumpy? Can you move to match the music?

P10 • Gather a selection of percussion instruments, including maraca
• Talk about how to make sounds on each of them. Do you blow, pluck, shake, hit or bang? Choose an instrument and then mime how to play it. Can your friends guess which instrument you are playing?

P12 • Look at some pictures of brass bands and listen to the instruments being played. Which sounds do you like? Why?
• Which sorts of animals would make a big sound like a tuba?

P14 • What sound does a tambourine make when you shake it? What sound does it make when you hit it?
• Close your eyes whilst a friend plays the tambourine. Can your guess if it is being shaken or hit?

P16 • Make little guitars using shoeboxes and elastic bands. Put a paper towel roll in the end of the shoebox to make the fingerboard. Use different widths of elastic bands. Do all the elastic bands make the same noise?

P18 • Play some Indian music and dance to it. Is the music fast or slow? Is it loud or soft?
• Tap out a simple rhythm using finger cymbals.

P20 • Have a go at playing a piano or keyboard. Play notes at each end of the piano. How are they different?

P22 • Sing the song, 'I am the Music Man'. Point to each of the instruments in turn while you sing. Can you remember what sound each makes?